WHAT A ?

By RUTH LEON
Illustrated by MAMORU FUNAI

A GOLDEN BOOK • NEW YORK
Western Publishing Company, Inc., Racine, Wisconsin 53404

 GOLDEN®, GOLDEN & DESIGN®, A FIRST LITTLE GOLDEN BOOK®, and A GOLDEN BOOK® are trademarks of Western Publishing Company, Inc. Library of Congress Catalog Card Number: 80-85078 ISBN 0-307-10102-9 / ISBN 0-307-68102-7 (lib. bdg.)

P Q R S T

WHAT AM I?

I am small.
I am furry.
I wash myself with my tongue.
I say *Mew-mew!*
What am I?

a frog?

a kitten?

a mouse?

a bear?

I am a **KITTEN**.
I step lightly on padded paws.
I like to play with balls of yarn.

WHAT AM I?

You put me on when you get dressed.
Usually I am made of leather.
You wear me on your feet.
What am I?

I am a pair of **SHOES**.
I keep your feet warm and dry.
Sometimes I squeak when I am new.
Can you tie me?

WHAT AM I?

I have a red comb and fine tail feathers.
I live in the barnyard.
I eat grain.
What am I?

a goat?

a pig?

a rooster?

a mouse?

I am a **ROOSTER**.
I say *Cock-a-doodle-doo*
early in the morning.
Sometimes I wake people up.

WHAT AM I?

I have many cars.
I run on a track.
I take people from one place to another.
What am I?

a train?

a fire engine?

a dump truck?

an airplane?

I am a **TRAIN**.
A big engine pulls me.
The engineer drives me fast down the track.
My wheels go *Clackety-clack*.

WHAT AM I?

I am big and gray.
I am very strong.
I have a long trunk.
What am I?

I am an **ELEPHANT.**
I have big ears.
I swing my trunk from side to side.
I spray water on my back with my trunk.

WHAT AM I?

I am round.
I grow on trees.
You can eat me.
Sometimes you drink my juice.
What am I?

a balloon?

a ball?

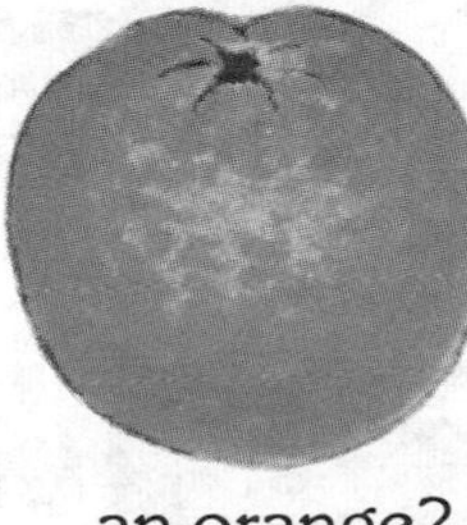

an orange?

a banana?

I am an **ORANGE**.
You can peel me.
Yum, yum! I taste good!

WHAT AM I?

I live on the farm.
I eat grass.
I give you milk.
I say *Moo, moo.*
What am I?

a hen?

a cow?

a lamb?

a pig?

I am a **COW.**
Every morning the farmer milks me.
I graze in the pasture all day.
At night I sleep in the barn.

WHAT AM I?

I can hop.
I have two long ears.
I like to eat lettuce.
What am I?

a duck?

a raccoon?

a rabbit?

a turtle?

I am a **RABBIT.**
I have soft fur.
I nibble carrots in the garden.

WHAT AM I?

I have four legs.
I stand in the bedroom
You sleep in me.
What am I?

I am a **BED**.
Sheets and blankets cover me.
You like to jump on me—
But not too often, please.

WHAT AM I?

I have a wet nose.
I wag my tail.
I say *Bow-wow!*
What am I?

a deer?

a monkey?

a dog?

a fish?

I am a **DOG.**
I like to chew bones.
I fetch sticks when you throw them.

WHAT AM I?

I am soft and fuzzy.
I have a head and arms and legs.
You like to play with me.
What am I?

I am a **TEDDY BEAR.**
I am warm and cuddly.
You like to hold me.
Sometimes you take me to bed with you.